Essential
First Aid
for Dog Owners

Other books available from All Publishing Company:
www.allpublishingcompany.com

Pot-Bellied Pet Pigs, Mini-Pig Care and Training
by Kayla Mull and Lorrie Blackburn, DVM
                        (aka Lorrie Boldrick, DVM)

Veterinary Care of Pot-Bellied Pet Pigs
by Lorrie Boldrick, DVM
(aka Lorrie Blackburn, DVM)

Pygmy Goats: Management and Veterinary Care
by Lorrie Boldrick, DVM

The Barefoot Veterinarian
by Lorrie Boldrick, DVM with Michael Boldrick, PhD

Essential
First Aid
for Dog Owners

A concise guide to caring for
man's (and woman's) best friend

By Lorrie Boldrick, DVM
for Freedom Dogs

Published by:

All Publishing Company
2387 N. Flanders St.
Orange, CA 92685

Copyright 2009 by Freedom Dogs, Inc.
and All Publishing Company
First Printing, March 2010
All Rights Reserved
Printed in the United States of America

ISBN: 0-9624531-5-3

The information contained in this book is not intended as a substitute for professional veterinary medical advice, emergency veterinary treatment, or formal veterinary first aid training. Don't use this information to diagnose or develop a treatment plan for a health problem or disease without consulting a qualified veterinarian. If you're dog is in a life-threatening or emergency medical situation, seek veterinary medical assistance immediately.

The first aid recommendations in this book will work most of the time as an initial immediate response to an injury. However, all dogs are different and will react differently to handling and treatment in various situations. Always use caution and common sense when performing any type of first aid on your dog. Always seek help from a qualified veterinarian and/or an emergency veterinary facility when your dog is injured. First aid is exactly that, first aid. It is not a substitute for qualified veterinary care.

Dedication

To all Freedom Dogs - present and future - their
trainers and their military partners.

www.freedomdogs.org

A special Marine with his special Freedom Dog.

Table of Contents

Foreword

I am honored to write an introduction to "Essential First Aid for Dog Owners."

First, this book is dedicated to an incredible organization which trains dogs to be companions to our young men and women who have served and put themselves in harm's way. What better way for man's (and woman's) best friend to offer help and comfort.

Second, Dr. Lorrie Boldrick is an incredible veterinarian and person. I have watched her work and trust her judgment and caring implicitly. There are many dog books out there, but this one gives practical, useful knowledge that anyone can follow.

Finally, some of the dogs illustrating the book live with me and my wife, Beth. I think you will enjoy the pictures of techniques that really work and can be very useful in an emergency.

Congratulations to Lorrie for this useful book.

David B. Hoyt, MD, FACS
Executive Director
American College of Surgeons
Chicago, IL

HEROES FOR DOGS OUR HEROES

Freedom Dogs

Freedom Dogs offers custom-trained specialty service dogs to wounded members of the military returning from armed conflict. Over 40,000 military personnel have been injured in the conflicts in Iraq and Afghanistan, and it is reported that 40% of all returning troops suffer from post-traumatic stress disorder (PTSD). Many of these returning men and women are so mentally, physically or spiritually broken that they have little hope of returning to mainstream life.

Freedom Dogs' unique Partner Program pairs a service dog and trainer team with these heroes as an adjunct to their rehabilitation on a short-term basis. The Freedom Dogs teams help reintegrate these young men and women back into society and normal activities of daily living.

Additionally, Freedom Dogs offers specially trained dogs for permanent placement with deserving warriors.

You can see videos and news clips of these dogs and their heroes at work at www.freedomdogs.org.

Freedom Dogs is a 501c3 non-profit organization.

Meribeth Russell
Director/ Lead Trainer
Freedom Dogs
www.freedomdogs.org

Preface

In December, 2008, I retired from my practice of veterinary medicine and transitioned to the position of Veterinary Advisor for Freedom Dogs (www.freedomdogs.org). The mission of Freedom Dogs is "Speeding the recovery and enhancing the lives of wounded military heroes through the use of specialty-trained service dogs." I am honored to be working with this young, growing organization and their special "freedom dogs" as they assist men and women returning from war in a very unique way.

As part of my role of Veterinary Advisor, I presented a talk on First Aid for the Freedom Dogs' trainers at their twice yearly training seminar. It was a fun opportunity which culminated in a powerpoint presentation accompanied by a short hand-out. The presentation was well-received and has evolved into this book.

The original presentation was intended for trainers of service dogs. But, "first aid is first aid." It doesn't matter if your dog is "just" a beloved pet or if he is an actively working service dog. If he is injured or sick, he may need you to administer first aid, or you may use this information to help a total stranger's dog. If you and I can help just one dog through a difficult health situation, then my writing and your reading of this book is worthwhile.

I've tried to make this book short and to-the-point. It is only intended to help you make educated decisions on how to handle emergency situations - in many cases while on the way to your veterinarian. There are many other books available on general care of your dog. This book will help you with real emergencies as well as perceived emergencies that aren't really so bad in the end.

A companion website has been created for this book at www.essentialfirstaidfordogowners.com. This website will contain updated information as medical recommendations change. We will also post videos of some of the procedures that are hard to explain with still pictures alone.

A thank you goes to Beth Russell, Founder of Freedom Dogs, for encouraging me (forcibly) to write this book and for continually nagging me to improve it. Equal thanks goes to my sister, Jane Bryant (my sister who lives in Kentucky), for her tireless editing of this book. She made me use common English words and only let me add some of my more technical terms in parentheses. I whined and fussed about all the changes - but I do like the end result and hope you do too. And thanks to my brother, Mikey, who also made lots of suggestions to improve the whole idea of the book and to improve the cover and style. They were all very patient with me during the process of preparing this book.

I also thank Tish Flynn, Connie Sweet, Chris Waggoner, Patti Mix, Jennifer Dent, and Karen Krusen for being willing to read early copies and make excellent suggestions for improvement.

I want to thank all the people involved with Freedom Dogs, as well as the Marines who are benefitting from the dogs, for including me in their organization. I am proud to be helping in my own small way. And by buying this book you are helping too.

Half of the proceeds from the sale of this book will be going directly to Freedom Dogs.

LB
March, 2010
Orange, CA

First aid is the immediate care given to a pet who has been injured or is suddenly taken ill.

Know your dog

It is natural to be worried and more concerned about a sick dog than a healthy one. However, knowing your healthy animal well is the best way to be alert to the earliest signs of any health emergencies. Subtle changes in behavior may alert you to the possibility of an illness before there are any other visible signs. You can then follow through with a more thorough evaluation of your animal's condition to decide if professional help or treatment is necessary.

The key to this is knowing your dog. This doesn't mean knowing the normal values of breathing and heart rates, although they will be discussed shortly. This means knowing your dog's normal behavior patterns, attitudes, posture, etc. If your dog usually demands her dinner at exactly 6pm and today she doesn't; if she usually barks at the mailman and today she doesn't; if she's avoiding petting and usually she demands it - why? These questions may all have answers that are unrelated to health problems. But these questions should come to mind. None of these situations should be ignored or left unanswered.

If you try to answer the above questions and don't come up with simple answers like "your husband/wife fed her half an hour ago" or "she's tired from a very long hike in the mountains," then you need to check the animal over more carefully.

1. First, stand back and observe. Are there any other changes you notice? Is she coughing, straining, preferring to lie down, pacing, circling, etc? Is she shivering or is her hair coat "puffed" up? Is she eating dinner or treats?
2. Now check her temperature and breathing.
3. Roll an eyelid out slightly and look at the color of the mucus membrane on the inside. It should be pink.
4. Check to see if there is a recent stool in the back yard. Is it normal for her?

Put all your signs together, come up with a tentative diagnosis, and if necessary call your veterinarian with the information. It would be wise to write your findings down so you don't forget any of them when you talk to the veterinarian.

By observing that your dog is less than 100% normal, you may be able to take action to prevent a serious problem. By checking her out carefully and thoroughly, you will be prepared to answer any questions your veterinarian may have if you find it necessary to contact her or him. It's far better to waste a few minutes of your time on a healthy dog who was just acting weird than to lose her because of inattention.

Spend a little extra time each day just observing your dog. Sit with her for a quiet "study" time. It's fun and relaxing and you may notice something important. "It's a tough job - but someone has to do it"!

Your first awareness of abnormal behavior may be accidental. We've all gone through our day, done our doggie chores and then realized that "something wasn't right." For example, in retrospect you realize that the water bowl was still full - and she always drinks over half the bowl. Pay attention when you get vibes that something is wrong. Follow through and find the source of the problem.

By training your pet to accept/ tolerate certain behaviors common to a veterinary examination, you will offer her a more positive approach to good health. You will also make your veterinarian very happy. Train your pet to accept/ tolerate many veterinary procedures. Teach your dog to accept being in a crate, being on a slippery table, being pushed, prodded and manipulated by a stranger (e.g., open the mouth, hold the feet tightly, lift the tail, put your fingers in the ear, etc.), being in strange positions (e.g., on his back and on his side with people standing over him), and being comfortable with other people both with and without your presence. These "tricks," will help ensure a positive experience by both your dog and your veterinary staff.

If your dog has been trained for all the above behaviors, she will be much less stressed when she needs treatment at a veterinary clinic. Stress makes diagnosis and treatment more difficult - both on the dog and on the veterinarian and veterinary staff.

Be alert to potentially dangerous situations for your dog. These include:

- Poisons
- Airbags (don't let your dog sit in the front seat)
- Riding in the back of a truck

Finally, prevention is the key to "Essential First Aid." The best first aid technique is the one you never have to use.

- Keep a journal of abnormal events or actions you observe with your dog.
- Record individual events, how often they happen and how long they last.
- Record possible triggering events, for example, different foods, travel, new surroundings, new people, etc.

Normal dog values

Temperature
- 100.5-102.5 °F

Breathing
- 10-30 breaths per minute

Heart Rate (Normal resting rates)
- Small dogs: 90-120 bpm (beats per minute)
- Medium dogs: 70-110 bpm
- Large dogs: 60-90 bpm
- Puppies - heart rate is higher and may be as high as 160 normally

Temperature

A dog's normal temperature will vary between 100.5° and 102.5°F. An individual animal may tend to have a normal temperature at one end or the other of the listed range, but for general purposes, any temperature readings within this range can be considered normal.

A temperature that is lower than 100.5° may also be a sign of disease or it may mean that the thermometer was in the middle of a stool and not in contact with the wall of the rectum.

Expect the temperature to be at the high end of normal if it is taken in the heat of the day.

Taking your dog's temperature
- Use a digital thermometer.
- You must take your dog's temperature rectally.
- Lubricate the end of the thermometer with vaseline, KY jelly, or water.
- Gently insert the thermometer just ½ - 1 inch inside the anus. Keep the thermometer parallel to the backbone. Don't push too far!
- If it is hard to push in, don't force it.
- Remove the thermometer and re-lubricate it.
- Try again.
- Leave the thermometer in place until it beeps (about a minute).

5

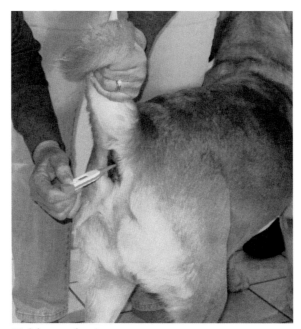

Taking a dog's temperature.

Breathing (respiration)

Respiration can vary greatly depending on the dog's emotional state. The normal respiratory rate is 10-30 breaths/ minute. The respiratory rate can be easily taken by watching the rib cage movement and counting the number of breaths per minute. An alternate method is to feel the respiration rate with your hands lightly in contact with the dog's rib cage. A highly excited animal will have a higher rate than "normal"" so use a little common sense and allow for variations with circumstances. Dogs will often be panting; if this is the case, record the rate as "panting" and don't try to count individual breaths.

6

Feeling for respiratory rate

Heart rate (pulse)

A dog's heart rate will vary depending on her size, level of exercise and emotional state. It can also be difficult to take. Practice on your dog when nothing is wrong. If you can't feel a pulse, ask your veterinarian to help you.

Ways to find a heart rate:

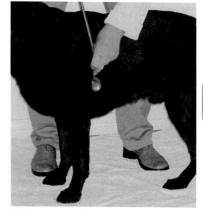

- It is easiest to take the heart rate with a stethoscope and count the number of beats per minute. Technically, this is the "heart rate."
- Since most people do not have a stethoscope, you can also feel for heart rate by holding your fingers tightly over the area of the heart near the bottom and front of the chest.

Using a stethoscope to listen to the heart.

- With a little practice, you can take a heart rate by feeling over the femoral artery on the inside of the hind leg up near the groin. You would probably need someone to show you just where to feel the first time.

- Always feel for the heart rate with your index and middle fingers - not with your thumb.

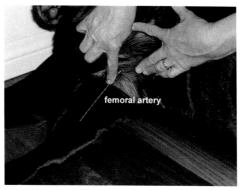

femoral artery

Pointing to the location at which you would take the heart rate of this dog.

Feeling the heart rate inside the hind leg.

Being ready for emergencies

- Have a first aid kit. (See Appendix B)
- Know poisons - have a poisonous substance reference handy. (See Appendix C)
  - Prevention of ingestion or other contact with a poisonous substance is far better than treating for a toxicity.
- Carry an information card (and program your cell phone). Include your veterinarian's name and number and basic information about your dog. A template to do this can be found on www.allpublishingcompany.com/firstaid.

8

Owner: Jane Doe
Phone: **555-123-4567**

Veterinarian: **Good Veterinarian, DVM**
Address: **1234 Any Street**
               Orange, CA
Phone: **555-567-8901**
Poison Control: 1-888-426-4435 ($60/call)
  or 1-800-213-6680 ($35 per call)

This is a
Freedom Dog

Dog's Name: **Freedom**
Birthday: **1/01/05**   Breed: **Labrador**
Sex: **M-neutered** Color: **Black**
Medications: **none**

Restraint and handling methods

Handling an Injured Animal

Any animal, even your own, this is injured or in pain can bite or scratch you. Even the friendliest of pets must be handled with care for the safety of all involved.

If your animal is injured, you must restrain him for your safety as well as his. Muzzle your pet to restrain him unless he is unconscious, has difficulty breathing, is vomiting or has a mouth injury.

> If you are accidentally bitten or scratched, seek medical attention. Both dog and cat bites can become infected quickly!

The following are different ways to restrain a dog.

Use a leash:

- With your own dog, attach his leash to his collar.
- With strange dogs, make a slip noose in the end of a leash or rope and drop it around the dog's neck.

Dropping a slip noose over the dog's head.

Apply a muzzle:
With your own dog, you may not need a muzzle. But remember that when he is in severe pain or when very frightened, even your own animal may bite you or someone helping you.

1. Speak and move calmly and quietly.

2. Have someone restrain the dog with a leash (if you have qualified help).

3. Approach the dog from the side and behind its head; do not attempt to put the muzzle on from the front.

4. Quickly slip a nylon or wire cage muzzle over the nose, secure snugly behind the ears.

If a muzzle is not available, you can make one from a strip of gauze, rag, necktie, belt, panty hose or soft, non-abrasive rope about 3 feet long.

1. Make a large loop in the center. Quickly slip the loop over dog's nose.

2. Bring the ends under his chin. Tie snugly behind his ears. (Always tie a muzzle tight.)

3. Never fully trust a muzzle. It is amazing how well dogs can remove them.

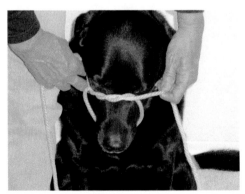 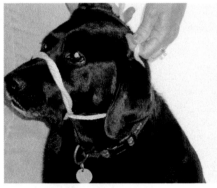

Starting the muzzle.   Finishing the muzzle.

Some dogs will not allow a muzzle to be put on them. Back off and take the dog to a professional or call animal control.

10

Use a towel:
Use a towel to help restrain a smaller dog. Wrap it around his head and neck.

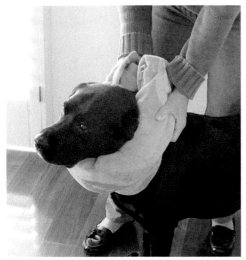

A towel "collar" for restraint.

Here's another way to use a towel to help restrain a dog.

Use a headlock:
A headlock can be used to control your dog while the veterinarian or another person works on the dog.

A headlock method of restraint.

11

Lay him on his side:
Use this to restrain your dog for treatment or examination of legs or side.

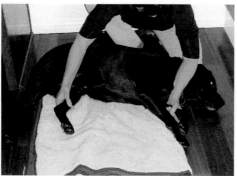 

Side restraint.

Close-up of side restraint.

Your arm goes over the neck and your hand holds the lower leg. If the dog is good, you just rest. If he is trying to get up, you pull up on your hand and push down with your forearm. Your other hand is keeping his back end from twisting back to get his legs underneath himself.

Carrying:
- If you suspect a hind end injury, hold under the chest and belly. Place your forearm between the front legs so you support the dog by his chest.

Holding under chest and belly.

Holding under chest and hind legs.

- If you suspect an abdominal injury, hold under the chest and hind legs. Place your forearm between the front legs so you support the dog by his chest.
- If you suspect a back injury, use a stretcher.

Bandaging

Bandages are used for several reasons:
- To protect wounds from the environment.
- To protect the environment from wounds.
- To discourage the pet from licking or irritating a wound.

Use antibiotic ointment or powder on the wound, cover with a gauze sponge when possible, then wrap firmly - but not tightly - with gauze and cover with a self-adherent bandage material such as vetwrap or Coban .

13

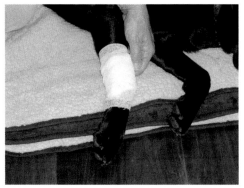
Gauze wrap over a gauze pad.

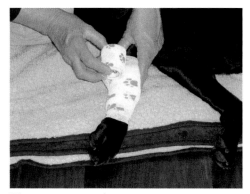
Vetwrap over the gauze.

A pressure bandage may be needed if there is a lot of bleeding and it needs to be controlled. Place a clean sanitary napkin or stack of gauze sponges over the bleeding wound and then tightly wrap as instructed above. Immediately take your dog to a veterinary facility for further care. A pressure bandage should not be left on any longer than necessary and your veterinarian can decide how else to control the bleeding.

CPR (Cardiopulmonary resuscitation)

We all know about CPR in humans, and we see it regularly on television hospital shows. On TV, it almost always seems successful. Fortunately, the need for CPR in animal emergencies is rare. Unfortunately, more often than not, CPR in dogs is unsuccessful - especially away from a veterinary hospital. That said, don't give up without trying if it is indicated.

CPR is ONLY administered to animals that are not conscious, not breathing AND have no pulse (heartbeat). The animal will be unconscious, totally limp and non-responsive.

14

Proper resuscitation (in humans and animals) follows the ABC's.

A. AIRWAY - make sure the animal has an open airway.
   1. Lay him on his right side and gently extend the head and neck.
   2. Pull the tongue forward between the front teeth.
   3. Make sure there is no foreign matter or vomit in the mouth.

B. BREATHING - when you are assured of an open airway, see if the dog is breathing.
   1. If he is breathing, then it is almost 100% guaranteed that his heart is also beating and you do not need to administer CPR.
   2. If he is not breathing, you must administer mouth to nose resuscitation.
      a. Hold his muzzle closed and place your mouth over his nose.
      b. Exhale into his nose until you see his chest rise. Do not blow too hard or too long. Only blow hard enough to make the chest rise.
      c. Give 4-5 breaths quickly and check to see if he starts breathing on his own.
   3. If he does not start breathing on his own, continue giving him breaths at 20 breaths per minute until you reach a veterinary facility.

Proper position of hands to administer CPR.

C. CIRCULATION -

1. Lay the dog on his right side.

2. Cup your hands over each other and place them just behind the dog's left elbow at the widest part of the chest.

3. Extend your elbows so your arms are straight.

4. Push down and compress the chest. Do this 80-120 times per minute (2 times per second).

5. Continue to give him breaths while doing chest compressions.

   a. Give one breath for every 5 compressions.

If you are unable to get your dog to a veterinary facility, or if you are so exhausted that you can no longer perform CPR appropriately, you should stop. The chances of survival after 15 – 20 minutes of CPR are very slim. You should take comfort in the fact that you did all that you could do with the resources available.

Puppy performing CPR.
Picture downloaded from Photobucket.com on Sept 10, 2009.

Injuries and illnesses

The following codes are used for recommended response times in first aid:

🐾   Take your dog to your veterinarian in the next few days.

🐾🐾   Take your dog to your veterinarian today or tomorrow - at the first available appointment.

🐾🐾🐾   Take your dog to the nearest emergency veterinary facility immediately.

Abscess

An abscess is a localized accumulation of pus.

Signs: Soft or firm swelling often with a "soft spot" over one area.

Treatment:

🐾   1.   If the abscess opens and drains on its own:

- Flush well with full strength hydrogen peroxide.
- Protect the dog's eyes when flushing the wound.
- **Do not allow the pus to run into the eyes or ears**.
- Do NOT try to force the abscess open by yourself.
- Have it checked by your veterinarian for follow-up treatment.

🐾🐾   2.   If the abscess does not open and the dog is lethargic take him to your veterinarian.

 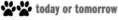

Bee stings / Insect bites

Most insect bites or bee stings cause a single area of localized swelling and redness. However, if your dog stumbled on an ant hill, there may be multiple smaller reactive spots.

Treatment:

- If you see the bite or sting happen or at the first sign of swelling from a suspected bite or sting, give diphenhydramine (Benadryl®) orally at 1 mg per pound. For an adult Labrador, this will be two 25mg capsules which are available over the counter in the drug store. There is a liquid form available if your pet is under 25 pounds.
    - Diphenhydramine can be repeated once in the morning and once at night for 2 days if needed.
- If you see a bee stinger - do **NOT** attempt to pull it out.
    - Instead, scrape it out carefully with a credit card. You are trying to avoid squeezing more of the poison into the dog.
- 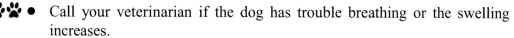 Call your veterinarian if the dog has trouble breathing or the swelling increases.

17

Arrow points to swelling from bee sting.

bee stinger

Scraping out bee stinger with a credit card. (Bee stingers are quite small and can be difficult to see.)

KEY
to pawprints

TAKE YOUR DOG TO THE VETERINARIAN:

| 🐾 in the next few days | 🐾🐾 today or tomorrow | 🐾🐾🐾 immediately |

Bite wounds (from other dogs)

Bite wounds can be a puncture or a superficial or deep cut. A small, deep puncture wound can be more serious than a superficial cut since it is more likely to close over and hold infection inside. The more open wounds, even though larger, are easier to keep clean.

Treatment:

- Clean a puncture wound with hydrogen peroxide or clean water. Keep it open for 5-7 days by scraping the scab once or twice daily. Apply a first aid cream twice daily.
  - If the puncture is deep, the dog should be on oral antibiotics also.
- Small cuts should be treated similarly to punctures, but may also require sutures.
- Larger wounds should receive veterinary advice.
- Deep cuts should be flushed and pressure should be applied if they are bleeding. A sanitary napkin or gauze pads work well for a temporary pressure bandage.

Bleeding

Blood loss may be visible (external bleeding) or may occur hidden within the body (internal bleeding).

<u>External bleeding:</u>
- You may see blood on the dog's fur or on the ground.
  - A little blood on the dog and on the ground *looks* like a lot.
  - Be clinical and not emotional when evaluating the amount of bleeding.

19

The "spot" is 1/4 cup of liquid.

The "spot" is 1 cup of liquid.

> The average 70 pound Labrador Retriever has a total blood volume of almost 3 quarts (12 cups). He can lose about 1.5-3 cups of blood quickly with no major health consequences. He should receive IV fluid replacement as soon as possible, however.

KEY
to pawprints

TAKE YOUR DOG TO THE VETERINARIAN:

🐾 in the next few days | 🐾🐾🐾 today or tomorrow | 🐾🐾🐾🐾🐾 immediately

Treatment:

1. Calm the dog as much as possible - this will decrease his blood pressure and slow the bleeding.

2. Muzzle the animal. (See page 10)

3. Press a thick gauze pad or sanitary napkin over the wound. Hold firmly or bandage firmly until clotting occurs. Hold for at least 3 minutes before checking to see if clotting occurred.

 4. If bleeding is severe and uncontrollable by other means, apply a tourniquet between the wound and the heart.

    - A **tourniquet is dangerous** and should only be used in life-threatening bleeding from a leg. It may result in amputation or disability of the limb.
        - If you must use a tourniquet, loosen it for 20 seconds every 15-20 minutes.
    - Use direct pressure over the wound rather than a tourniquet whenever possible.

If you are trimming your dog's toe nails and cause one to bleed, you can apply a styptic powder to help it clot more quickly. It probably will clot on its own if you don't have your styptic powder handy.

<u>Internal bleeding</u>
Signs: Bleeding from nose, mouth, rectum; coughing blood; blood in urine; pale gums; collapse; rapid or weak pulse. Sometimes no blood may be visible.

Treatment:

1. Keep animal as warm and quiet as possible. Wrap dog in warm, dry towels (the towels can be warmed in a dryer).

2. If unconscious, keep head level with rest of body.

 3. Take to nearest veterinary facility immediately.

 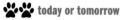

Bloat

Bloat is a life-threatening condition in which the stomach fills with air (dilatation) and may twist upon itself (torsion).

Signs: Drooling, panting, abdominal swelling, attempted vomiting and restlessness.
- Often occurs within hours of a meal.
- Can quickly lead to shock.

21

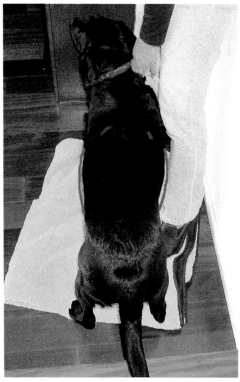

The red lines show where you should look for abdominal swelling.

Treatment:
 **Emergency - take to nearest veterinary surgical facility immediately!!!**
- There is no first aid that will help.

Breathing problems (dyspnea)

Signs: Increased effort to breathe, noisy breathing, a bluish tinge to the lips and mucous membranes (cyanosis), inability to breathe in or breathe out.

Treatment:
This will vary remarkably depending on the cause of the breathing problem.

- If your dog is breathing with difficulty, but is not distressed (i.e., he will readily take a treat when offered), no treatment may be necessary.
- Long-term, chronic breathing difficulties are often due to pneumonia or other lung abnormalities. The specific problems should be diagnosed and treated by your veterinarian.
- Airway obstruction, or partial obstruction, may be caused by severe allergic reactions causing swelling of the airways themselves. Keep the dog calm and seek immediate veterinary assistance.
- A foreign object such as a stick, ball, or piece of food caught in the throat requires your help. See "Choking" (page 24). Take him immediately to the nearest veterinary facility.

> Do **NOT** put your fingers in the mouth of a conscious dog who cannot breathe - you **will** be bitten.

22

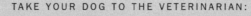

Burns

Burns may be caused by heat, flame, chemicals, or electricity.

Treatment:

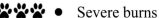 • Mild to moderate burns

    1. Muzzle the animal (see page 10).

    2. Flush immediately with large quantities of cold water.

    3. Apply topical first aid cream or burn ointment.

• Severe burns

    • Muzzle the animal (see page 10).

    • Quickly apply ice water compresses.

    • Treat for shock if necessary (see page 37).

    • Take immediately to the nearest veterinary facility.

23

Choking

Choking can be caused by something caught **in** the throat or pressing **on** the throat.

Signs: Coughing/ gagging, head extended forward, increased breathing effort, pale or blue mucus membranes.

Treatment:
- If he can cough, let him try to dislodge the obstruction on his own.
- If he is not coughing, try the abdominal thrust maneuver.
    1. Straddle the dog and grip your hands together under him, just behind the chest (back of ribcage).
    2. Pull up sharply 2-3 times.

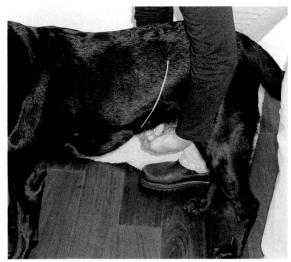

Clasp your hands together and pull up sharply. The white line indicates the back of the ribcage.

- If the dog collapses and passes out, look in his mouth and try to remove any visible object that can easily be plucked from the mouth with two fingers.
    - ○ If none can be found, go immediately to the nearest veterinary facility.
- **Do not waste too much time** attempting to remove the obstruction yourself before taking him to a veterinarian.

Dehydration

The abnormal loss of water from the body, especially from illness or physical exertion. Excessive vomiting, diarrhea, or panting may cause dehydration in your dog.

Signs: Loss of skin elasticity, eyes sunken, dry mucus membranes, shock, collapse - depending on level of dehydration. You can test for dehydration by "tenting" the skin. If you pull up the skin and it stays there, rather than dropping back to a normal position, then the dog is dehydrated.

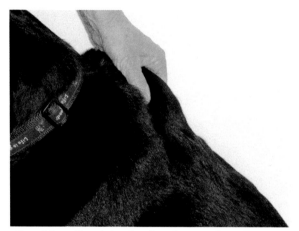

Checking for dehydration by tenting the skin.

Treatment:
- Offer clean, fresh water, but do not allow the dog to drink too much or too quickly. Drinking too quickly will cause him to vomit, which will increase the dehydration.
- Keep offering small amounts.
- 🐾🐾 Give liquids such as Pedialyte or Gatorade that contain electrolytes instead of plain water if possible.
- 🐾🐾🐾 If he refuses to drink, take him immediately to a veterinary facility.

Diarrhea

Diarrhea is an extremely loose stool and can be caused by overeating, eating bad food such as garbage, bacterial or viral infections and other diseases. Diarrhea can be very soft or it can be very watery. Unless the diarrhea is watery, it is more messy than unhealthy.

Treatment:

If the dog is acting normally:

1. Give no food by mouth for 24 hours.

2. Then, if the dog is willing to eat, offer him 1/4 ration of a bland food and increase to normal quantities in 24 hours.

3. If he refuses food or if the diarrhea stays watery (as opposed to very soft) for over 24 hours, take him to your veterinarian. You do not want him to become dehydrated. **Remember to take a stool sample also**.

4. If the stool stays abnormally soft for over 48 hours, it is important to find and treat the cause of the problem. Take your dog and a stool sample to your veterinarian. You may be able to prevent a recurrence of the problem.

If the dog is not himself, for example, he is lethargic, acts like his stomach hurts, or has not been eating, go immediately to your veterinarian.

> Note: After a bout of watery stools, your dog may not pass any stool for over 24 hours. This is to be expected.

26

Drowning (Near drowning)

Signs: Difficult and exaggerated breathing, pale / blue mucus membranes, loss of consciousness - after spending a lengthy time in and sometimes under the water.

Treatment:

- 🐾🐾🐾 • If the dog is having any trouble breathing, take him immediately to the nearest veterinary facility.

- 🐾🐾🐾 • If he is unconscious, hold him up by the hindquarters so water can run out the nose and mouth, and take immediately to the nearest veterinary facility. If he is not breathing, follow the guidelines for CPR.

27

Drowning can occur if your dogs are not fairly equal in size and swimming capability.

Ear problems

Signs: Shaking head, scratching at ear, blood or other material oozing from the ear canal, foul smell to ear. Ear problems are very common in dogs and can be caused by foreign bodies, bacterial or yeast infections, or just inflammation.

Treatment:

🐾 ● Clean visible material from ear - use alcohol or hydrogen peroxide. Schedule an appointment with your veterinarian.

28

🐾 ● If the ear flap is swollen (ear hematoma), leave it alone. Schedule an appointment with your veterinarian for an ear examination.

🐾🐾 ● If the ear flap is bleeding, apply direct pressure to the spot for 5 minutes. If it continues to bleed, bandage the ear over the head and go to your veterinarian. The thigh portion of a pair of panty hose with a hole cut for the good ear to stick out makes a good bandage (snood).

A bandage (snood) applied to protect the right ear.

KEY to pawprints   TAKE YOUR DOG TO THE VETERINARIAN:
🐾 in the next few days | 🐾🐾 today or tomorrow | 🐾🐾🐾 immediately

Electrocution

Electrocution most commonly occurs when puppies chew on electrical cords.

Signs: Drooling, ulcers in mouth, shock, collapse.

> **Do not touch the dog until the electrical source has been turned off or moved**. This is to avoid injury to yourself.

Treatment:

- Turn off the electrical source. Once the electrical source is disconnected, take your dog immediately to a veterinary facility.

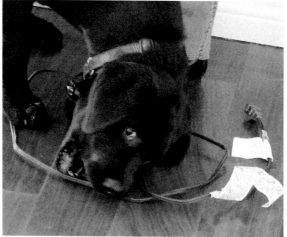

Don't leave electric cords where your dog can chew on them.

Eye injuries

Signs: Squinting or protecting the eye, any abnormal appearance of the eyeball, the eyelid cannot cover the eyeball, any suspected trauma to the eye.

Treatment:
- Flush the eye with sterile saline or contact lens rewetting solution. It is ok to use clean, room temperature water if no saline is available.
- If the eye stays squinted or becomes reddened, take him to see his veterinarian.

Fainting/dizziness (syncope)

This is not an immediate emergency if it occurs once and the dog recovers quickly. By quickly I mean within 30-60 seconds. Remember that those 30-60 seconds will have seemed like an hour to you. Make an appointment with your veterinarian for a full examination and blood sample in the next few days.

Fever

A fever is generally a temperature higher than 102.5°F.

Signs: The dog may act normally or may be panting, uncomfortable, agitated, depressed.

Treatment:
1. If your dog has a temperature of 103° or above for more than 12 hours or if there are any other symptoms of illness, schedule an appointment with your veterinarian.
2. If the temperature is over 104°, go to the nearest veterinary facility immediately.

Fracture

Signs: Sudden, severe lameness with swelling and pain in the affected leg.

Treatment:
- Muzzle the animal. (See page 10)
- Do not attempt to set the fracture - just stabilize it by applying a splint.
- **If you are not absolutely sure where the bone is fractured, do not apply a splint.** Veterinarians often see a dog with a broken leg and a splint that is applied below the fracture - so it actually makes things much worse.
- If there is excessive bleeding from a fracture wound, apply a moderate pressure wrap to that area - under the temporary splint.
- Putting on a splint
  1. Wrap the broken leg in cotton padding or a clean washcloth or hand towel.
  2. Wrap with a magazine, rolled newspaper, towel or two sticks. The splint should extend one joint above the fracture and one joint below.
  3. Secure with tape.
  4. Make sure the wrap does not constrict blood flow.
- 🐾🐾🐾 If the spine, ribs, or hips (any body part that can't be wrapped) appear injured or broken, gently place the animal on a stretcher and keep the dog as still as possible.
- 🐾🐾🐾 For any kind of fracture, go to the nearest veterinary facility.

31

Hyperthermia (heat stroke, heat prostration)

Signs: Body temperature over 104 degrees, excessive panting and salivation, decreased consciousness, diarrhea, collapse

Treatment:

 • Cool the dog off with cold wet towels and immediately take him to the nearest veterinary facility.

- ○ Rewet and replace the towel frequently. Do not put a cold wet towel on the dog and just leave it. It will become a sauna as it heats up from the dog's high temperature.
- ○ Apply ice water or very cold water to the dog's feet. Dogs sweat through their feet.
- ○ You can also apply ice water to the thin skin in the groin and lower belly of the dog.

Use a cold, wet towel to cover the dog. Spread the ice around on his groin and feet primarily.

Hypothermia

Signs: Body temperature below 100.5 degrees, decreased heart rate, pale mucus membranes, shivering, coma.

Treatment:
- Wrap dog in warm towels (the towels can be warmed in a dryer).
  - **Give nothing orally while the body temperature is below normal.**
- Take to nearest veterinary facility immediately.

33

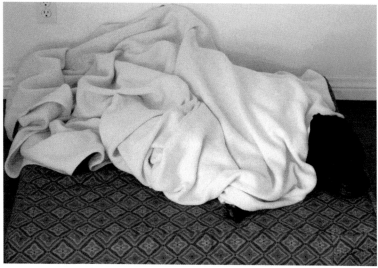

Use a warm, dry towel or blanket to cover the dog.

Impalement injuries

Dogs frequently carry sticks in their mouths and are impaled when an end of the stick jams into the ground. They may also attempt to jump over pointy objects and accidentally land on them, or occasionally be on the receiving end of a jab with a stick or knife from an evil human.

Treatment:
1. Do NOT pull out any object that is sticking out of your dog. Even porcupine quills **must** be removed by a veterinarian.
2. Cut the object off with just a few inches extending from the wound.
3. Minimize movement of the object and do not pull it out.
4. Take immediately to the nearest veterinary facility.

34

> Exception: You may safely remove cactus spines. It is easiest if you use a pair of needle-nose pliers and grab the spine close to the dog's skin.

Two cactus spines in this dog's muzzle.

Poisoning

If you suspect that your dog has eaten something poisonous, look for evidence that some of the substance is missing. Figure out how much and approximately when it was eaten.

Keep the container if possible or at least get the brand name, active ingredient name and any information on the package regarding poisoning treatment.

Signs:

- It is best to start treatment prior to seeing any signs.
- Signs are dependant on the poisonous substance.
  - Signs could be vomiting, diarrhea, tremors, seizures, or any combination.
- Signs may not show up for many hours after contact with some toxic substances.

Treatment:

1. Call veterinarian or poison control center for recommended treatment.
   a. Have the container or package available when you call.
   b. ASPCA Poison Control phone number: 1-888-426-4435 ($60 per call)
   c. Or Pet Poison Helpline: 1-800-213-6680 ($35 per call)
2. If instructed, induce vomiting.
   a. Give hydrogen peroxide orally at 1 teaspoon (5cc) / 10 lbs.
   b. Repeat in 15 minutes if vomiting has not occurred.
3. If instructed, give activated charcoal.

Prevention is far better than treatment. Keep your animals away from toxic substances. Remember that dogs can be very ingenious about getting into things that you thought were safely put away.

- For more information on poisons refer to Appendix C.
- You can also use the internet.
  - Go to http://aspca.org. Click on Pet Care then Animal Poison Control
  - Or go to http://petpoisonhelpline.com

Seizures / convulsions

Signs: Loss of control of some or all body parts, may be unable to stand, may lose consciousness.

Treatment:
1. Observe the dog - and try not to be emotional.
   a. Does it start on one side?
   b. Does the dog lose consciousness?
   c. How long does the seizure last? It will seem to take forever, so you have to use a watch for this.
2. Be sure that the dog is in a safe place where he cannot fall off a piece of furniture or into a pool and will not get his leg entangled in chair legs.
3. Do NOT put your hand in his mouth. Dogs will not "swallow their tongues," but they may close their mouth during a seizure, and if your hand is in it, you will be bitten.
4. Keep a record of any seizures with careful descriptions of the seizure, length of the seizure, and circumstances surrounding the seizure. Call your veterinarian to see what follow-up he/she recommends.

Shock

Shock often accompanies severe injury or extreme fright.

Signs: Weak pulse, increased heart rate, shallow breathing, cold legs, or dazed appearance.

Treatment:

🐾🐾🐾 **The key to successful overall treatment is prompt veterinary care.**

37

- Keep animal restrained, quiet and warm. Wrap dog in warm, dry towels (the towels can be warmed in a dryer).
- Stabilize any additional injuries, for example, put pressure on bleeding.
- If unconscious, keep head level with rest of body.
- Take immediately to the nearest veterinary facility.

Snakebite

If your dog is "struck" by a snake, assume it is a poisonous bite.

Treatment:

- Keep the dog as calm as possible.
- Put on gloves and wash the wound with mild soap and water.

 - Take immediately to a large emergency veterinary facility. They are the most likely place to have anti-venom in stock.

- It is helpful if you can identify the species of the snake - but do not attempt to catch or handle it.
  - If you have a digital camera or a cell phone - **take a picture of the snake**.

38

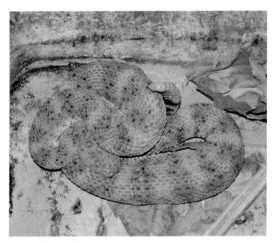

A rattlesnake in a garage.

- **Do NOT attempt to suck out the venom.**
- **Do NOT use a tourniquet.**

Prevention:

- Snake avoidance training. Classes are offered in many areas with rattlesnakes. These classes teach your dog to recognize rattlesnakes by sight, smell and sound and then to stay away from them. An electric shock collar is used, but if your dog will possibly come in contact with a rattlesnake, the shock collar may be the lesser of the evils.
- Rattlesnake vaccine is available in some states. Once vaccinated, the dog has some protection against snake venom and will have a better chance of making it to a veterinary clinic for more classic treatment. Check with your local veterinarian.

Vomiting

Many dogs will vomit/ gag up a little bit of water if they drink too quickly. This is normal. If the dog is vomiting more than this, you need to take action.

Treatment:

- 🐾🐾 If you know the dog has eaten something he shouldn't have like a bone, cloth, baby bottle nipple, etc. take him to your veterinarian.
- If you are not aware of any cause of the vomiting, withhold all food and water for 24 hours.
  - ○ If it is a very hot day, keep him inside in a cool environment so he doesn't dehydrate more than just from the vomiting.
- 🐾🐾 **If he is still vomiting in 8 hours or is feeling "awful," take him to your veterinarian.**
- If he quits vomiting for 24 hours:
  1. Start him on 1/4 cup of water.
  2. If he keeps that down for an hour, increase the water to a cup.
     - ○ Keep offering water every half hour until he leaves some water in the bowl. Then fill the bowl for him.
  3. Slowly add 1-2 tablespoons of food every couple of hours.
  4. He can be back on normal rations in another 24 hours.
- 🐾🐾 If at any point he starts vomiting again, take him to your veterinarian.

39

Wounds

Treatment:

With external wounds, evaluate the depth and extent of the wound.

- Very small or superficial wounds: clean well with hydrogen peroxide or warm water and apply a first aid cream.
  - May not need additional veterinary care.
- Minor wounds: clean well and apply a light bandage.
- Major wounds: if possible, put a clean wrap, such as a washcloth or t-shirt, over the wound before taking to a veterinarian.
  - If the wound is bleeding excessively, use a pressure bandage.

40

A t-shirt can work very well as a wrap prior to going to the vet or as a bandage to prevent chewing on an incision or healing wound.

Euthanasia

Euthanasia is often referred to as "putting your dog down" or "putting your dog to sleep." The word euthanasia actually means "good death."

There comes a time when your love and care and your veterinarian's professional care can no longer give your dog a good quality of life. Start thinking about that time before it comes. Make an intellectual choice of what quality of life means to your dog - and be ready to stand by that choice. When the decision needs to be made, you will tend to lean toward your emotional decision rather than your intellectual one. As a veterinarian, I would rather euthanize a dog a week too early rather than a day too late. Don't be a day late for your dog.

41

Appendix A - Giving medication

Pills can be the easiest to give. If your dog is a good eater, put the pill in a small amount of food and hand it to her. It is always wise to have a second treat in your hand so she will swallow the first piece of food quickly to make room for the next. Sounds easy? Then, there is the dog who refuses the treat. In that case:

1. With one hand, hold the dog's upper jaw just behind the canine teeth and push the lips in to encourage him to drop his lower jaw a bit.

2. With the other hand, which is holding the pill, push the lower incisor teeth down and insert the pill into the back of the mouth on the center of the tongue.

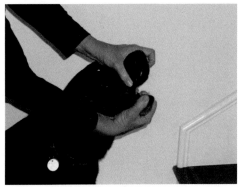

Opening the mouth. Note that the lips are wrapped in over the teeth

Inserting the pill to the back of the mouth.

3. Close the mouth and hold it closed until she swallows the pill. You can tell she swallowed when she licks.

4. Don't let go too soon or the pill may quickly be back out on the floor.

Cheating is OK! Give the pill with a spoonful of peanut butter, cream cheese or whatever your dog likes!

Liquid medications are usually administered with a plastic eyedropper or syringe.
1. Suck in the appropriate amount of medication.
2. Insert the end of the syringe into the pocket between the lips and the back teeth of the dog.
3. Slowly squeeze in the medication.
4. Keep the dog's head level. Do NOT tip it up.

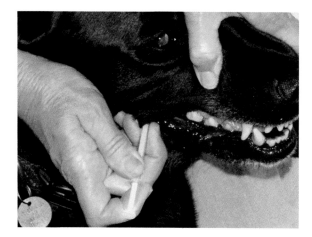

If the dog absolutely refuses to swallow the medication, you would rather have it drip out onto the ground (and your clothes) than have him inhale any of it.

If he doesn't fight, but also doesn't swallow, try pushing the syringe tip in a bit further so it goes between the teeth slightly. This will encourage swallowing.

If a little bit of the medication does drip out, don't worry unless the dose was very small. If you have any questions, call your veterinarian to be sure.

Topical medications are easy to apply, but can be tougher to keep applied. Dogs like to lick and remove any foreign substance from their body - if they can reach it. Ask your veterinarian if it is safe to apply the medication with your fingers. Apply the medication and rub it in well (unless told otherwise by your veterinarian). Then feed the dog or take her for a walk to distract her from her desire to remove the medication. By the time the walk is over, she will most likely have forgotten all about the medication. If not, you will have to be creative in designing a T-shirt or bandage to protect the area treated. You can also use an Elizabethan collar to protect wounds from your dog's tongue.

44

A soft Elizabethan collar is much more comfortable than the old plastic "E. Collars."

Eye medications are often a challenge unless your dog is very well behaved. It is important to get the medication onto the eye without doing additional damage to the eye.

<u>Eye drops</u> are the easiest to administer.
1. Tip the dog's head back slightly and hold the eye open with one hand.
2. With the other hand, hold the dropper bottle above the eye and squeeze out one or two drops.

    a. Do not touch the eye with the bottle.

45

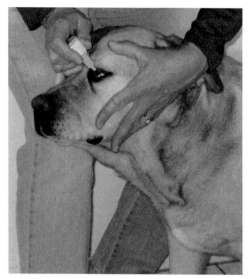

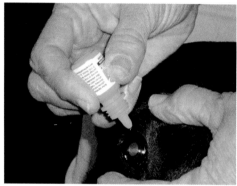

A closer view of applying eye drops.

Applying eye drops.

<u>Eye ointments</u> are a bit trickier to administer.
1. Hold the dog's head up and the upper eyelid up with one hand.

2. Put the tip of the tube up over the white of the eye and squeeze out 1/4 inch of medication.

3. Allow the eye to close, then open and close the eyelids several times which will cause the medicine to "melt" and cover the eye.

46

Applying an eye ointment.

An uncooperative dog will challenge the best of us to apply an eye ointment safely. Sometimes you can squeeze the 1/4 inch of medicine onto the tip of your finger and then "roll" it in under the upper eyelid. Or you may just have to become a dog trainer and teach the dog to allow the medication to be applied!

Ear medications are usually needed because of a sore ear and the dog may be quite protective of that ear. So be gentle and be prepared. The ear canal of a dog goes straight down a short way and then makes a right angle turn in toward the head. Most medications need to get all the way to the bottom to that horizontal canal.

1. Lift the dog's ear flap.

2. Insert the tip of the bottle or ointment tube into the ear canal.

3. Aim the tube straight down.

4. Squeeze in the appropriate amount of medication.

5. Then massage the area below the opening of the ear (over the vertical ear canal) well.

47

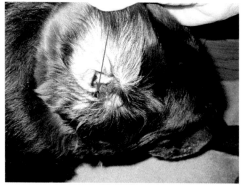

The arrow points at the opening into the ear canal.

Notice how the ointment tube is aimed down into the ear canal.

The dog will shake her head after this, so don't try to stop her. And most especially, don't get into a battle of strength with the dog - win the battle by outsmarting her or by reaching an agreement with her. Don't try to out-muscle her.

Massage below the ear canal to get the medication to move down into the deep canal.

Appendix B - First Aid Kit

The following are some suggested contents for your dog first aid kit. You may want to pack the contents into a small backpack for ready access.

Bandaging materials:
2 & 4 inch vetwrap (or Coban®)
Cotton padding
Gauze pads
Gauze rolls
Sanitary napkin
Scissors

Drugs:
Activated charcoal (Toxiban®)
Alcohol (rubbing 70%)
Antibiotic powder/ ointment
Diphenhydramine (Benadryl®)
    (use liquid form if your dog
    is under 25 lbs)
Eye lubricant
Eye wash
Hydrogen peroxide
Styptic powder

Miscellaneous:
List of emergency phone numbers
First aid book
Exam gloves

Clean cloth and towel
"Space blanket" (if no warm blanket is
    available)
Instant cold pack
Cotton rope
Nylon leash
Muzzle
Panty hose (as a muzzle or bandage)

Can of favorite wet food
Gatorade packets

Thermometer
Tweezers
Needle nose pliers with wire cutter
Dog nail clippers
Q-tips
Small flashlight or penlight
Syringe, 5cc

Appendix C - Poisons / dangerous items

Here is a list of some of the more common poisons affecting dogs. If you think your dog got into any of the listed items, then call your veterinarian for more detailed information. You may also call Poison Control.

Foods
Alcoholic beverages
Avocado
Caffeine
*Chocolate
Coffee
Fatty foods
Garlic
*Grapes
Macadamia nuts
Milk
Moldy or spoiled foods
*Onions, onion powder, chives
Products sweetened with xylitol
*Raisins
Salt
Undercooked meat, eggs, bone
Yeast dough

Medications
Acetaminophen
Anti-cancer drugs
Antidepressants
Cold medications
Diabetes drugs
Diet pills
*NSAIDS (ibuprofen)
Narcotics (Vicodin®)
Pseudoephedrine
Vitamin D derivatives
Vitamins

*see page 51 for toxic amounts of these items.

Poisonous Plants
Amaryllis
Autumn Crocus
Azalea / Rhododendron
Castor Bean
Chrysanthemum
Cycad Palms
Cyclamen
Daffodils
English Ivy
Foxglove
Holly
Kalanchoe
Lilies
Marijuana
Mistletoe
Oleander
Peace Lily
Pothos
Sago Palm
Schefflera
Tulip / Narcissus bulbs
Yesterday, Today, and Tomorrow
Yew

49

This is NOT a comprehensive list. When in doubt, call your veterinarian or poison control.

Miscellaneous Poisons

Animal toxins—toads, insects, spiders, snakes and scorpions
Antifreeze
Baits - Rat and mouse, slug and snail
Batteries
Blue-green algae in ponds
Christmas tree water
Citronella candles
Cocoa mulch
Compost piles / Fertilizers
Fabric softener sheets
Flea products
Fly baits
Household cleaning products
Liquid potpourri
Mothballs
Oil-based paints
Polyurethane glues
Pennies after 1982
Swimming-pool treatment supplies

Other dangerous items

Electrical cords
Glass ornaments
Ribbons, tinsel, or yarn

The following items are NOT poisonous

Cat litter
Glow jewelry
Glue traps
Pennies prior to 1982
Poinsettia
Silica gel packets
Toilet bowl water (even with most constant release cleaners)
Water-based paints

> This is NOT a comprehensive list.
> When in doubt, call your
> veterinarian or poison control.

Toxic Doses:

Weight of Dog	5 lbs	10 lbs	15 lbs	20 lbs	25 lbs	30 lbs	50 lbs	75 lbs	100 lbs
Milk chocolate - ounces	5	10	15	18	22	27	45	67.5	90
Dark chocolate - ounces	1.5	3	4.5	6	7.5	9	15	22.5	30
Baking chocolate - ounces	0.6	1.2	1.7	2.2	2.8	3.4	5.6	8.4	11.4
Grapes - ounces	2.5	5	7.5	10	12.5	15	25	37.5	50
Grapes - individual	7	14	21	28	35	42	70	105	140
Raisans - ounces	0.25	0.5	0.75	1	1.25	1.5	2.5	37.5	5
Onions - ounces	1.25	2.5	3.75	5	6.25	7.5	12.5	18.75	25
Ibuprofen - milligrams	125	250	375	500	625	750	1250	1875	2500

Appendix D - References

ASPCA Poison Information,
http://www.aspca.org/pet-care/poison-control

AVMA - Disaster Preparedness
http://www.avma.org/disaster/saving_family.asp

Christmas Poison Handout, Advanced Critical Care and Internal Medicine, Tustin CA, 2004

Pet Poison Helpline, http://petpoisonhelpline.com

Sue Ailsby, Training Advisor for Freedom Dogs
http://www.dragonflyllama.com

Index

www.freedomdogs.org

About the Author

Lorrie Boldrick, D.V.M.

Dr. Boldrick is a Southern California veterinarian specializing in small animals, including dogs and cats as well as small livestock (goats, sheep and pigs) and many exotics, such as monkeys, birds, snakes, wallabies, mountain lions, llamas, emus and dolphins. In addition to her own practice, she has served as the on-call veterinarian for Disneyland, Knott's Berry Farm, the Orange County Fair, the Santa Ana Zoo, the Orange County Zoo and several other local parks, aquariums and zoos. Her personal collection (menagerie) of pets has been almost as diverse as those she has treated, reaching a maximum of over fifty critters at one time. She was the president of the National Pygmy Goat Association and is an active member of the American and Southern California Veterinary Medical Associations.

Made in the USA
Coppell, TX
18 July 2021